LON

This I-SPY book belongs to:_____

London is one of the greatest cities in the world. Its long history and endless variety make it a fascinating city to explore.

Evidence of London's past is all around – and is easy to spy. There are sections of Roman settlement still visible in the City dating back 2000 years; the Tower of London dates back 1000 years to William the Conqueror. Sir Christopher Wren's masterpiece, St. Paul's Cathedral dates from the 17th century; the London Eye and the Gherkin are only a decade old and form part of the modern landscape of the changing city.

It has too much history and is too large for anyone to know it all but, with I-Spy London, you can get to know it very well – and go on to discover more things for yourself. There are so many places to see and explore and the best way to explore London is on foot. The Underground also means you can move about

Introduction

London easily for variety, perhaps seeing the East End in the morning and Buckingham Palace in the afternoon. Buses are interesting, too, as are the launches on the Thames and Regent's Canal.

For Outer London, trains are usually best. The Underground is great for visitors who soon come to treat it like a reliable friend. Londoners certainly do – it kept more than 180,000 of them safe during one night of the Blitz in 1940!

To get the best from your visit remember:
• Do not try to see too much in one day – you will enjoy it more if you take it easily.
• Children should always be accompanied by an adult, never alone.
• Take care crossing the roads, London is a very busy city.

How to use your I-SPY book

The book is arranged by area to help you get the best out of your visit, the maps at the rear of the book will help you achieve this. As you explore, don't forget to tick off the sights – as you see them. You need 1000 points to send off for your I-Spy certificate (see page 64) but that is not too difficult because there are masses of points in every book. As you make each I-Spy, write your score in the box and, where there is a question, double your score if you can answer it. Check your answer against the correct one on page 63.

SHERLOCK HOLMES MUSEUM

The interior of the fictional address of the great detective at 221b Baker Street, has been faithfully maintained exactly as described in the published stories.

I-SPY points: 10

Date: _____

LONDON ZOO

London Zoo, in Regent's Park, is one of world's most famous zoos and home to over 12,000 animals. 'Meet the Animals' shows are held daily, giving visitors the opportunity to learn more about the animals from their keepers.

I-SPY points: 10

Date: _____

MADAME TUSSAUDS

A major London attraction – no ropes or barriers allow for real close-up photo opportunities of the famous – and infamous!

I-SPY points: 10

Date: _____

BBC BROADCASTING HOUSE

The headquarters of the BBC and home to Radio 3, Radio 4 and Radio 7. Some BBC music radio stations are based next door in Western House.

I-SPY points: 20

Date: _____

REGENT STREET

One of the most famous streets in London, Regent Street is well-known for its annual Christmas lights, usually switched on by a celebrity during the first week of November.

I-SPY points: 10

Date: _____

REGENT'S PARK

One of the Royal Parks of London and a lovely place to stroll. London Zoo is contained within the northern boundary of the park.

I-SPY points: 10

Date: _____

OXFORD STREET

Oxford Street is one of most famous shopping streets in the world. Always busy, take a look at the ultra modern crossing at the junction with Regent Street.

I-SPY points: 5

Date: _____

SELFRIDGES

First opened in 1909, Selfridges department store has recently undergone a major facelift and dominates the west end of Oxford Street.

I-SPY points: 10

Date: _____

THE WALLACE COLLECTION

Masterpieces by Titian, Rubens, Reynolds, Van Dyke and Canaletto line the rooms filled with fine furniture and porcelain.

I-SPY points: 20

Date: _____

MARBLE ARCH

This edifice, originally built as the entrance to Buckingham Palace, was moved to its current location in 1851.

I-SPY points: 10

Date: _____

SERPENTINE LAKE

Peace and serenity is never very far away in London. You can take a rowing boat out on the man-made lake and admire the views.

I-SPY points: 15

Date: _____

HYDE PARK

A public park since early in the 17th century, Hyde Park is one of London's most prized open spaces. It has hosted many major music festivals.

I-SPY points: 10

Date: _____

PRINCESS DIANA MEMORIAL FOUNTAIN

Located in the south-west corner of Hyde Park, this is not a fountain in the traditional sense, it is actually a large oval stream bed about 50 x 80m.

I-SPY points: 15

Date:

SPEAKERS' CORNER

Located at the north-east side of Hyde Park, Speakers' Corner is a space for orators and hecklers to debate the issues of the day.

I-SPY points: 10

Date:

PETER PAN STATUE

The boy who never grew up is immortalised in a bronze statue in Kensington Gardens.

I-SPY points: 15

Date:

9

ROYAL ALBERT HALL

A major arts venue hosting classical music (including the world famous Proms), rock, ballet, tennis and award ceremonies. It is one of the most atmospheric music venues in the world.

I-SPY points: 15

Date:

ALBERT MEMORIAL

Gleaming in gold leaf following a major restoration project, the Albert Memorial is dedicated to Queen Victoria's husband who died in 1861.

I-SPY points: 15

Date:

HARRODS

I-SPY points: 10

Date: _____

Perhaps the most famous shop in the world. It boasts a huge array of products – the food hall on the ground floor houses a vast selection of food stuffs from the exotic to the everyday. Make sure you allocate plenty of time to visit!

HARVEY NICHOLS

Another iconic Kensington store. Indulge yourself on three floors of fashion or head to the Fifth Floor restaurant.

I-SPY points: 10

Date: _____

VICTORIA AND ALBERT MUSEUM

Referred to as the V&A, this fine museum is housed on four floors. Endless galleries display fine and applied art collections, sculpture, furniture, fashion and photographs.

I-SPY points: 15

Date: _____

SCIENCE MUSEUM

A vast collection of mechanical, electronic and power exhibits. Modern features include the Apollo 10 command module and Digitopolis – an entertaining look at modern technology.

I-SPY points: 15

Date: _____

NATURAL HISTORY MUSEUM

This vast museum contains hundreds of exciting interactive exhibits with sections on ecology and the animal world.

I-SPY points: 15

Date:

KENSINGTON PALACE

A royal residence since the 17th century. Today it is the official residence to several royals including the Duke and Duchess of Gloucester and the Duke and Duchess of Kent.

I-SPY points: 15

Date:

ST JAMES'S PARK

Once one of Henry VIII's many hunting grounds, the park is overlooked by the impressive Tudor gatehouse of Henry's palace (1530).

I-SPY points: 10

Date:

ST JAMES'S PALACE

Dating back to the first half of the 16th century, this building was designed as a royal residence. Occupied by high-ranking Crown servants since 1922, Queen Elizabeth II made here first speech as queen here.

I-SPY points: 15

Date:

FLORENCE NIGHTINGALE STATUE

The Lady with the Lamp is located just off The Mall.

I-SPY points: 15

Date:

GREEN PARK

Green Park opened to the public in 1826 and today is a popular open space for early morning joggers and walkers.

I-SPY points: 10
Date: _____

THE RITZ

One of the most famous hotels in London. The experience of afternoon tea may be a little formal so pop into the foyer and see where the rich and famous stay.

I-SPY points: 15
Date: _____

EROS

The statue of Eros, located in Piccadilly Circus, is believed to be the first in the world to be cast in aluminium.

I-SPY points: 10
Date: _____

FORTNUM AND MASONS

Fortnums first opened in 1707 and continues to be world famous for its high quality goods. It was the first store in the world to sell Heinz baked beans – in 1886!

I-SPY points: 15

Date: _____

BEADLES AT BURLINGTON ARCADE

The Beadles are a private police force located in the Burlington Arcade and can be identified by their Edwardian frock coats and top hats.

I-SPY points: 20

Date: _____

BOND STREET

'Old' and 'New' Bond Street is home to many upmarket fashion boutiques and jewellers.

I-SPY points: 10

Date: _____

ROYAL ACADEMY OF ARTS

The Academy stages big, thematic shows and is famous for its summer exhibition.

I-SPY points: 15

Date:_____

PICCADILLY CIRCUS

Located at the junction of Piccadilly and Regent's Street, Piccadilly Circus has long been a focal point in central London, famous for its neon advertising signs and home of the statue of Eros. It is particularly colourful at night.

I-SPY points: 10

Date:_____

ADMIRALTY ARCH

A large building located between The Mall and Trafalgar Square. As the name suggests, traffic and pedestrians pass through an arch within the building.

I-SPY points: 15

Date:_____

17

BUCKINGHAM PALACE

The Queen's official residence has over 600 rooms and boasts a 42-acre garden. The palace's state apartments are open to the public in summer: tours include the Throne Room, the Picture Gallery and the State Dining Room. If the Royal Standard is flying overhead, the Queen is in residence.

I-SPY points: 10

Date: _____

CHANGING OF THE GUARD

A magnificent ceremony that takes place outside Buckingham Palace. Take up a good view point for some wonderful photographs!

I-SPY points: 15

Date: _____

VICTORIA MONUMENT

This large monument is a memorial to Queen Victoria who reigned from 1837 until her death in 1901, the longest of all British monarchs.

I-SPY points: 15

Date: _____

HORSE GUARDS PARADE

Originally Henry VIII's tournament ground, a mounted guard is ceremonially changed here twice a day.

I-SPY points: 15

Date: _____

THE MALL

The Mall is famous the world over as "The Red Road". It runs from Buckingham Palace to Admiralty Arch.

I-SPY points: 10

Date: _____

SHEPHERD MARKET

Tucked away, this part of Mayfair is a collection of cobbled lanes full of cafes, small shops and restaurants.

I-SPY points: 20

Date: _____

BERKELEY SQUARE

A large, rectangular open space, made famous by the song 'A nightingale sang in Berkeley Square'. London has many such squares where you can take a break and rest your feet.

I-SPY points: 15

Date: _____

CLARENCE HOUSE

Named after its first resident, William, Duke of Clarence, this house was designed by John Nash and dates from 1827. It is now the official residence of The Prince of Wales, The Duchess of Cornwall, Prince William and Prince Harry.

I-SPY points: 20

Date: _____

HAMLEYS

'Must-visit' for children, this fantastic toy store is housed over seven floors packed with every type of toy and game imaginable for every age range.

I-SPY points: 15

Date: _____

LIBERTY

Built in 1924, the mock-Tudor department store is a goldmine of fashion, cosmetics, ceramics and printed fabrics.

I-SPY points: 20

Date: _____

CARNABY STREET

The heartbeat of 'Swinging London' in the 1960s may have lost some of its original charm but is still a fashionable shopping street.

I-SPY points: 15

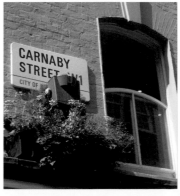

Date: _____

LEICESTER SQUARE

Lined with cinemas, the square is the scene of frequent celebrity-studded first nights.

I-SPY points: 10
Double points if you spot someone famous

Date: _____

THE TROCADERO

A huge entertainment centre packed with bright lights, shops, a cinema and lots of fun things to do.

I-SPY points: 10

Date: _____

PALLADIUM

Tucked away in Argyll Street, off Oxford Street, the London Palladium is probably the most famous theatre in the UK and the venue for many blockbuster productions.

I-SPY points: 20

Date: _____

TRAFALGAR SQUARE

The square is dominated by the façade of the National Gallery as well as the 50m (165ft) column dedicated to Admiral Lord Nelson. The base is guarded by four massive lions.

I-SPY points: 10

Date: _____

ST MARTIN-IN-THE-FIELDS

This lovely 18th-century building is the parish church of the royal family.

I-SPY points: 15

Date: _____

24

NATIONAL GALLERY

A Neo-Classical gallery with a superb collection of European paintings ranging from 1250 to 1900. The collection includes works by Botticelli, Leonardo da Vinci, Rembrandt, Gainsborough, Turner, Cezanne and Van Gogh.

I-SPY points: 15

Date: _____

NATIONAL PORTRAIT GALLERY

Visit to see history as art – portraits and representations of important figures throughout the ages, including English monarchs since medieval times.

I-SPY points: 15

Date: _____

Who is this famous man?

I-SPY points: 15

Date: _____

CHINATOWN

Best seen in the evenings. The oriental cuisine in this colourful area is the best in town!

I-SPY points: 10

Date: _____

WEST END THEATRES

Take in one of the many plays in London's Theatreland with many world famous shows.

I-SPY points: 10

Date: _____

MUSEUM OF LONDON

Extensive collection depicting the history of London, with excellent Roman artefacts from nearby excavations and superb displays on all periods.

I-SPY points: 15

Date: _____

FROST FAIR MURAL

Before the building of modern bridges, the River Thames often froze in winter. Underneath Southwark Bridge is a mural of the infamous Frost Fair of 1564.

I-SPY points: 25

Date: _____

ROYAL COURTS OF JUSTICE

These buildings handle many of the nation's major civil cases.

I-SPY points: 15

Date: _____

GUILDHALL

The administrative centre of the city for almost 900 years. The crypt and great hall date from the 15th century.

I-SPY points: 15

Date: _____

OLD BAILEY

This building is forever linked with crime and punishment. The new criminal courts opened in 1907.

I-SPY points: 15

Date: _____

LINCOLN'S INN FIELDS

Lincoln's Inn Fields is the largest public square in London. The chambers of many law firms surround the green area.

I-SPY points: 20

Date: _____

SIR JOHN SOANE'S MUSEUM

A private collection that includes an Egyptian sarcophagus and Hogarth's Rakes Progress.

I-SPY points: 20

Date: _____

BANK OF ENGLAND MUSEUM

Located at the rear of the Bank of England, the museum traces the history of the bank from 1694 to the present day with a fascinating collection of coins and notes.

I-SPY points: 20

Date: _____

TOWER BRIDGE

Tower Bridge has stood over
the River Thames since 1894
and is one of the finest, most
recognisable landmarks in the
world.

I-SPY points: 10

Date: _____

HMS BELFAST

A World War II cruiser, with nine
decks to explore – everything from
the Captain's Bridge to the massive
boiler and engine rooms.

I-SPY points: 15

Date: _____

TOWER OF LONDON

Originally built by William the Conqueror, the Tower of London has been a fortress, a prison, as well as a palace. The Beefeaters and famous ravens guard the priceless Crown Jewels.

What is the correct title of the Beefeaters?

I-SPY points: 10
Double with answer

Date: _____

BARBICAN

A monolithic cultural centre with an art gallery, cinema, theatre and auditorium.

I-SPY points: 15

Date: _____

TOWER 42

Built for the National Westminster Bank (its former name was the Nat West Tower) it was renamed Tower 42 by its new owners in reference to its 42 floors.

I-SPY points: 15

Date:

THE GHERKIN

Officially it's 30 St Mary Axe or sometimes the Swiss Re Building but most of us know it as the Gherkin!

I-SPY points: 10

Date:

ST PAUL'S CATHEDRAL

Christopher Wren's most famous monument was completed in 1708 and is the site of the tomb of Nelson and Wellington and has played host to a number of important royal occasions from Queen Victoria's Diamond Jubilee celebrations in 1897 to the marriage of Prince Charles and Princess Diana.

I-SPY points: 10

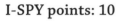

Date: _____

MILLENNIUM BRIDGE

The first new bridge across the river Thames since Tower Bridge opened in 1894, and the first ever for pedestrians only, the Millennium Bridge is now an established feature linking St Paul's Cathedral with the Tate Modern.

I-SPY points: 15

Date: _____

ST KATHERINE DOCKS

Built in 1828, the docks traded for over 120 years and were closed after larger ships could no longer pass through the lock into the basin. Following World War II damage the area was redeveloped and given new life.

I-SPY points: 15

Date: _____

THE MONUMENT

The monument stands 60.6m high and exactly 60.6m from the spot in Pudding Lane where the Great Fire started in 1666.

I-SPY points: 20

Date: _____

BIG BEN

Probably the most famous landmark in London, Big Ben is actually the name of the 14-tonne bell, cast in 1858, of the 4-faced clock (the largest in Britain) at the top of the Clocktower in the Houses of Parliament.

I-SPY points: 5

Date: _____

HOUSES OF PARLIAMENT

The seat of English government since 1512 and home to both the House of Commons and the House of Lords. This vast mock-gothic palace was built after a devastating fire destroyed the original building in 1834.

I-SPY points: 5

Date: _____

DOWNING STREET

This most famous of streets was built by Sir George Downing in 1680. Number 10 has been the official residence of serving British prime ministers since 1732.

I-SPY points: 10

Date: _____

OLIVER CROMWELL

Following the English Civil War, Cromwell took control of the country under the title Lord Protector. In 1649, Cromwell famously abolished Christmas!

What was Cromwell's nickname?

I-SPY points: 20

Double with answer

Date: _____

RICHARD THE LION HEART

King Richard I ruled from 1189-1199 and although he spoke little English and spent very little time in England he remains a much loved ruler.

I-SPY points: 20

Date: _____

SIR WINSTON CHURCHILL

This massive Parliament Square statue was erected in 1973 and depicts the wartime prime minister, Sir Winston Churchill – voted the greatest ever Briton in 2002.

I-SPY points: 15

Date: _____

THE CENOTAPH

Built in the 1920s by Sir Edwin Lutyens, this bleak stone memorial commemorates the dead of both world wars. Wreaths are placed here on Remembrance Sunday, which is the closest one to November 11th.

I-SPY points: 10

Date: _____

WESTMINSTER ABBEY

A site of worship for over 1,000 years. Originally a 10th-century Benedictine monastery, the 13th century abbey is the resting place of countless regal, military and literary names. Every monarch since William the Conqueror, except two, has been crowned under its roof.

I-SPY points: 10

Date: _____

STATUE OF BOUDICA

The warrior queen of the Iceni tribe rose up against the Romans in AD61. Her statue stands prominent on the embankment overlooking Westminster Bridge.

I-SPY points: 15

Date: _____

CABINET WAR ROOMS

Winston Churchill and the British government directed troops from here during the Blitz in World War II.

I-SPY points: 15

Date: _____

CLEOPATRA'S NEEDLE

Dating from 1475BC, the Egyptian needle stands on Victoria Embankment, completed in 1870.

I-SPY points: 10

Date: _____

BATTLE OF BRITAIN MONUMENT

The monument pays tribute to those who took part in the Battle of Britain, fought in the skies over Britain in World War II.

I-SPY points: 20

Date: _____

SOMERSET HOUSE

A major arts and cultural centre close to the River Thames. In winter the central courtyard is home to an open ice rink.

I-SPY points: 15

Date: _____

THE SAVOY

Having undergone a £150m refurbishment, the Savoy remains one of the world's finest hotels.

What is unusual about Savoy Court, the entrance road to the hotel?

I-SPY points: 15

Double with answer

Date: _____

WHITEHALL

A broad street running from Trafalgar Square to Parliament Square, it is the seat of political power and home to many civil servants.

I-SPY points: 5

Date: _____

TATE BRITAIN

Built by the 19th-century sugar magnate, this gallery houses art from the 16th to the 20th centuries.

I-SPY points: 10

Date: _____

LONDON EYE

Planned as a temporary exhibit for the Millennium celebrations, the London Eye has proved to be a firm favourite for visitors of all ages. On a clear day the 360-degree views are stunning.

I-SPY points: 5

Date: _____

LONDON AQUARIUM

Housed in County Hall, the London Aquarium hosts approximately 55 different aquatic displays, which hold 3,000 different forms of marine life.

I-SPY points: 10

Date: _____

SOUTHWARK CATHEDRAL

There has been a church on this site since 1086 although it did not become a cathedral until 1905. It houses the most interesting collection of tombs and epitaphs outside of Westminster Abbey.

I-SPY points: 20

Date: _____

TATE MODERN

This barn like art deco power station turned art gallery is Britain's national museum of modern art displaying major works by Matisse and Picasso as well as contemporary work, exhibitions and installations.

I-SPY points: 10

Date: _____

SHAKESPEARE'S GLOBE THEATRE

The original theatre has been lovingly recreated with materials, techniques and craftsmanship of 400 years ago.

I-SPY points: 15

Date: _____

OXO TOWER

When the makers of Oxo beef stock cubes wanted to advertise their product with large illuminated signs in the 1920s, they were refused permission. The result? Build your own advertising!

I-SPY points: 15

Date: _____

NEW SCOTLAND YARD

New Scotland Yard is the headquarters of the Metropolitan Police.

I-SPY points: 25

Date: _____

CLINK PRISON MUSEUM

Slang now for any prison, the museum in Clink Street illustrates the history of this infamous jail and the surrounding area.

I-SPY points: 25

Date: _____

IMPERIAL WAR MUSEUM

The Imperial War Museum tells the story of British military conflicts from World War I to the present day.

I-SPY points: 20

Date: _____

LONDON DUNGEON

Split in to six sinister sectors, the London Dungeon brings the gruesome history of London to life. Uncover the truth about the Great Plague, Jack the Ripper and the Great Fire of London.

I-SPY points: 15

Date: _____

BOROUGH MARKET

The fruit and vegetable market has existed since at least 1276, and has been on the current site since the mid 18th-century.

I-SPY points: 20

Date: _____

GOLDEN HINDE

In St Mary Overie Dock, you will find a full-size replica of Sir Francis Drake's galleon in which he circumnavigated the globe in 1577-1580.

I-SPY points: 20

Date: _____

IMAX

This large-format cinema, close to Waterloo Station, feature a screen 20 x 26m wide (66 x 85ft).

I-SPY points: 20

Date: _____

COVENT GARDEN

London's oldest planned square, dating from the 1630s and built over Lundenwic, a Saxon town only unearthed in the last 20 years.

I-SPY points: 10

Date: _____

ROYAL OPERA HOUSE

Home to the Royal Opera, the Royal Ballet and the Orchestra of the Royal Opera House.

I-SPY points: 15

Date: _____

LONDON TRANSPORT MUSEUM

Travel through time and learn the history of London's transport system, from 1800 to the present day. Most exhibits are child-friendly allowing for a close up inspection of old trams, buses and trains.

I-SPY points: 15

Date: _____

BRITISH MUSEUM

England's oldest museum opened in 1753; the archaeological splendour includes an array of finds from prehistoric and Roman Britain.

I-SPY points: 10

Date: _____

BRITISH LIBRARY

The national library of the UK is one of the world's largest research libraries. It contains over 150 million items and a copy of every book produced in the UK (including this one!).

I-SPY points: 15

Date: _____

BT TOWER

At a height of 160m (520ft) its Top of the Tower revolving restaurant was once one of the capitals' greatest attractions. It was closed for security reasons in 1980.

I-SPY points: 5

Date: _____

ST PANCRAS STATION

Renovated in the 2000s at a cost of £800 million, the refurbished station is the terminus for Eurostar™ services to and from Continental Europe.

I-SPY points: 10

Date: _____

I-SPY points: 10

Date: _____

BATTERSEA POWER STATION

The old power station has been crumbling away since shutting in 1983. The roofless structure has become an iconic sight on the south bank. There have been many proposals to redevelop the site.

I-SPY points: 15

Date: _____

CUTTY SARK

Built in 1869 as a clipper crossing both the Atlantic and Pacific Oceans, it has been moored up in dry dock since 1957 and offers a fascinating insight into the daily life of the merchant seamen. *Currently being restored following a major fire in 2007. Due to re-open 2011.*

WEMBLEY STADIUM

The world's most expensive football stadium hosts England international matches and major domestic cup games as well as pop concerts.

I-SPY points: 15
Double if you see a match here.

Date: _____

CANARY WHARF

Built on the site of the West India Docks, Canary Wharf contains three of the UK's tallest buildings.

Do you know their names?

I-SPY points: 20
Double with answer

Date: _____

O2 ARENA

Originally a temporary structure for the Millennium celebrations, the O2 is now a major indoor venue for concerts and performances.

I-SPY points: 20

Date: _____

REGENT'S CANAL

The canal, now mostly used by pleasure craft, runs from Little Venice near Paddington, through Regent's Park and London Zoo to Camden Town with its market.

I-SPY points: 20

Date: _____

NATIONAL MARITIME MUSEUM

The National Maritime Museum displays an unrivalled collection of maritime artefacts.

I-SPY points: 20

Date: _____

THAMES BARRIER

Built to stop London from flooding, its 10 futuristic gates are supported by seven concrete piers.

I-SPY points: 25

Date: _____

See which, on the following pages, you can I-Spy for 5 points each.

DRAGON

Date: _____

GUARD IN BEARSKIN

Date. _____

DOUBLE-DECKER BUS

Date: _____

NEWSPAPER SELLER

Date: _____

BLUE PLAQUE

Date: _____

UNDERGROUND SIGN

Date: _____

MAIN LINE STATION

Date: _____

BLACK TAXI

Date: _____

PHONE BOX

Date:

CHELSEA PENSIONER

Date:

BUSKER

Date:

CYCLE COURIER

Date:

ANY LONDON BRIDGE

Date:_____

ER SIGN

Date:_____

SOUVENIR STALL

Date:_____

BEEFEATER

Date:_____

LONDON MARATHON

Date: _____

PUNK

Date: _____

RIVER BOAT

Date: _____

PUB

Date: _____

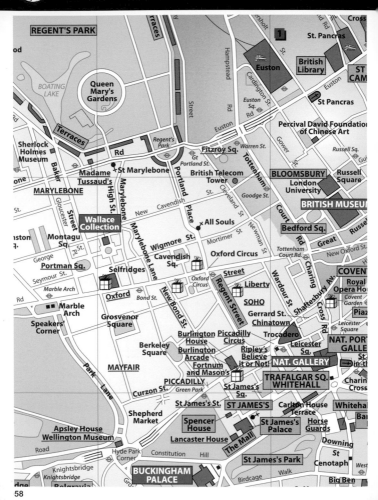

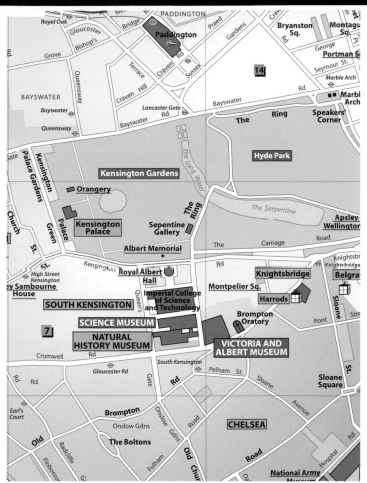

PADDINGTON

Royal Oak
Gloucester
Bishop's
Bridge
Paddington
Praed
Gardens
Bryanston Sq.
Montagu Sq.

Grove
Queensway
Terrace
Craven Rd
Sussex
George
Portman Sq
Seymour St.

BAYSWATER
Craven Hill
Bayswater
Lancaster Gate Rd
Bayswater
Bayswater
The   Ring
Marble Arch

Marble
Arch

Queensway
**Speakers'
Corner**

Palace Gardens
Kensington
Church St.
Kensington Gardens
The Long Water
Hyde Park

Orangery
Palace Green
**The
Ring**
The Serpentine

**Kensington
Palace**
**Sepentine
Gallery**
The Serpentine
**Apsley
Wellington**

Albert Memorial
The   Carriage   Road

High Street
Kensington
Kensington
Knightsbr
Knightsbridge

ey Sambourne
House
**Royal Albert
Hall**
Knightsbridge
Belgra

SOUTH KENSINGTON
**Imperial College
of Science
and Technology**
Montpelier Sq.

Harrods
Sloane
Stre

7
SCIENCE MUSEUM
**Brompton
Oratory**
Pont

**NATURAL
HISTORY MUSEUM**
**VICTORIA AND
ALBERT MUSEUM**

Cromwell   Rd
South Kensington
Pelham St.
Sloane
**Sloane
Square**

Gloucester Rd
Gate
Rd
Sloane
St.

Earl's
Court
Rd   Rd

Brompton
Onslow Gdns
Onslow Gdns
Road
Old
CHELSEA

Old
The Boltons
Fulham
Church
Road
Avenue

Radcliffe
Finborou
Hospital

**National Army
Museum**

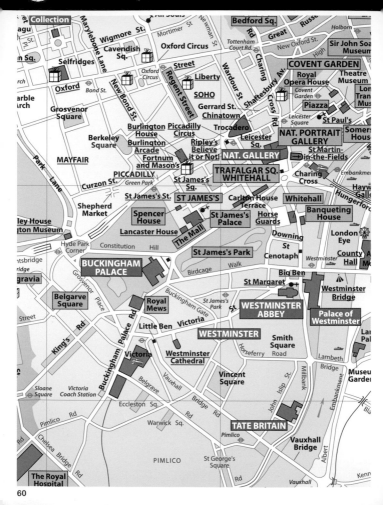

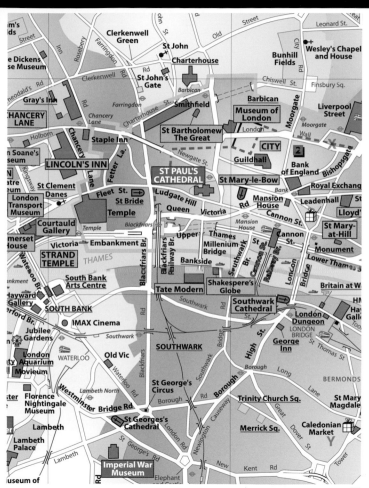

Clerkenwell
Green
Leonard St.
St John
Charterhouse
Bunhill
Fields
Wesley's Chapel
and House
Dickens
se Museum
St John's
Gate
Chiswell St.
Finsbury Sq.
Gray's Inn
Barbican
Smithfield
Barbican
Museum of
London
Liverpool
Street
St Bartholomew
The Great
CHANCERY
LANE
Staple Inn
CITY
Guildhall
Bank
of England
Bishopsga
Soane's
useum
LINCOLN'S INN
St Mary-le-Bow
Royal Exchang
St Clement
Danes
Ludgate Hill
Mansion
House
Leadenhall
London
Transport
Museum
Fleet St.
St Bride
Temple
Queen
Victoria
Cannon St.
Lloyd'
Courtauld
Gallery
Thames
Millenium
Bridge
Upper
Cannon
St.
St Mary-
at-Hill
ST PAUL'S
CATHEDRAL
Monument
Victoria Embankment
STRAND
TEMPLE
THAMES
Blackfriars
Railway Br.
Bankside
Lower Tham
Bridge
Blackfriars Br.
South Bank
Arts Centre
Tate Modern
Shakespere's
Globe
Britain at W
Hayward
Gallery
SOUTH BANK
Southwark
Cathedral
London
Dungeon
Ha
Gall
IMAX Cinema
Southwark
George
Inn
Jubilee
Gardens
SOUTHWARK
BERMONDS
London
Aquarium
Moviuem
WATERLOO
Old Vic
Borough
St Mary
Magdale
Florence
Nightingale
Museum
St George's
Circus
Trinity Church Sq.
Lambeth
St Georges's
Cathedral
Merrick Sq.
Caledonian
Market
Lambeth
Palace
Imperial War
Museum
Kent Rd.

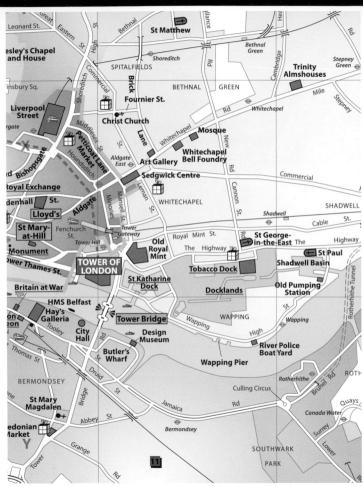

St Matthew

Leonard St.
Great Eastern St.
Bethnal
Bethnal Green
Alliance
Stepney Green
High St.
Shoreditch
SPITALFIELDS
Trinity Almshouses
Cambridge Rd
esley's Chapel and House
Commercial
Brick Lane
BETHNAL GREEN
Mile
Stepney
insbury Sq.
Shoreditch High St.
Fournier St.
Whitechapel
Liverpool Street
Middlesex St.
Christ Church
orgate
Bishopsgate
Petticoat Lane Market
Houndsditch
Mosque
Whitechapel Bell Foundry
New Rd
Royal Exchange
denhall
St.
Aldgate
Art Gallery
Aldgate East
Sedgwick Centre
WHITECHAPEL
Commercial
Lloyd's
Leman St.
Minories
Cannon St.
SHADWELL
St Mary-at-Hill
Fenchurch St.
Shadwell
Cable St.
Monument
Tower Hill
Tower Gateway
Mansell St.
Old Royal Mint
Royal Mint St.
The Highway
St George-in-the-East
The Highway
St Paul
ower Thames St.
TOWER OF LONDON
Tobacco Dock
Shadwell Basin
Rotherhithe Tunnel
Britain at War
St Katharine Dock
Docklands
Old Pumping Station
HMS Belfast
Hay's Galleria
Tower Bridge
WAPPING
on eon
Tooley
City Hall
Design Museum
Wapping
Wapping
Thomas St.
Butler's Wharf
River Police Boat Yard
High St.
BERMONDSEY
Druid St.
Wapping Pier
Rotherhithe
ROTH
St Mary Magdalen
Bridge St.
Jamaica Rd
Culling Circus
Brunel Rd
Quays
edonian Market
Abbey St.
Bermondsey
Canada Water
Surrey
Lower
Grange Rd
SOUTHWARK PARK

11

Index

First published by Michelin Maps and Guides 2010 ©
Michelin, Proprietaires-Editeurs 2010. Michelin and the
Michelin Man are registered Trademarks of Michelin.
Created and produced by Blue Sky Publishing Limited.
All rights reserved. No part of this publication may be
reproduced, copied or transmitted in any form without
the prior consent of the publisher. Print services by
FingerPrint International Book production – fingerprint@
pandora.be. The publisher gratefully acknowledges
the contribution of the I-Spy team: Camilla Lovell, Trey
Watts and Ruth Neilson in the production of this title.
The publisher gratefully acknowledges the contribution
of Sian Iddiols.

The publisher also gratefully acknowledges the
co-operation and assistance of the following who
supplied pictures for this title: David Boardman, London
Zoo, Unitaw Limited, Madame Tussauds, Matthew
Armstrong, Steve Cadman, Barbara Rich, Mary
Harrsch, London Dungeon, National Portrait Gallery,
Visit London, Ben Salter, London Transport Museum,
Imperial War Museum, Corbis Images, Bank of England
Museum. Other images in the public domain and used
under a creative commons licence. Mapping based on
Ordnance Survey of Great Britain with the permission
of the Controller of Her Majesty's Stationery Office ©
Crown Copyright 100000247

Reprinted 2012   10 9 8 7 6 5 4

Answers: P25 National Portrait Gallery, William Shakespeare, **P31** Tower of London, Yeoman Warders, **P36** Oliver
Cromwell, Old Ironsides, **P42** The Savoy, it is the only road in UK where vehicles are require to drive on the right,
P51 Canary Wharf, One Canada Square (Canary Wharf Tower), 8 Canada Square, Citygroup Centre.

HOW TO GET YOUR I-SPY CERTIFICATE AND BADGE

Every time you score 1000 points or more in an I-Spy book, you can apply for a certificate

HERE'S WHAT TO DO, STEP BY STEP:

Certificate

- Ask an adult to check your score

- Ask his or her permission to apply for a certificate

- Apply online to www.ispymichelin.com

- Enter your name and address and the completed title

- We will send you back via e mail your certificate for the title

Badge

- Each I-Spy title has a cut out (page corner) token at the back of the book

- Collect five tokens from different I-Spy titles

- Put Second Class Stamps on two strong envelopes

- Write your own address on one envelope and put a £1 coin inside it (for protection). Fold, but do not seal the envelope, and place it inside the second envelope

- Write the following address on the second envelope, seal it carefully and post to:

I-Spy Books
Michelin Maps and Guides
Hannay House
39 Clarendon Road
Watford
WD17 1JA